I'M WRECKED, THIS IS MY JOURNAL

For Mark, Matilda and Sam, who make
parenting the best job in the world

First published in Great Britain in 2017 by
Michael O'Mara Books Limited
9 Lion Yard
Tremadoc Road
London SW4 7NQ

A CIP catalogue record for this book is available from the British Library.

Papers used by Michael O'Mara Books Limited are natural,
recyclable products made from wood grown in sustainable
forests. The manufacturing processes conform to the
environmental regulations of the country of origin.

ISBN: 978-1-78243-819-9 in print format

1 2 3 4 5 6 7 8 9 10

www.mombooks.com

Designed by Claire Cater
Illustrated by Ellie O'Shea

Printed and bound by CPI Group (UK) Ltd, Croydon, CR0 4YY

I'M WRECKED, THIS IS MY JOURNAL

THE ALTERNATIVE BABY BOOK FOR FRAZZLED PARENTS

SHANNON CULLEN

Michael O'Mara Books Limited

THIS JOURNAL
BELONGS TO:

....

PARENT OF:

....

HOW TO USE THIS JOURNAL

This journal is designed to be
used in any order.

Just choose the page that feels
most relevant to your day.

You can record the date and note a sentence
that describes the day – maybe something
that happened or how you felt.

Laugh, cry or drink wine and remember
that all of these moments are memories
of your parenting adventure.

Share your pages with other parents
using #ImWreckedJournal.

DATES THAT YOU WILL NEVER REMEMBER OTHERWISE

BABY'S FIRST:

Smile

Tooth

Rolled over

Crawled

Walked

Word or animal noise

HEALTH DATES:

Immunizations

Check-ups

Appointments

Date: Today:

'Newborns don't blink. Don't freak out.'

Baby's name: ....

Time of birth: ....

Weight: ....

Date of birth: ....

Eye colour: ....

Hair colour: ....

The name of the person who delivered your baby was:

....

Five words to describe today: ....

....

....

....

Date: .... Today: ....

....

Draw and colour in your child's name here.

'You don't realize how many
people you dislike until
you have to name a baby.'

Date: _____   Today: _____

_____

_____

Who or where does your child's name come from?

Which other names were on your shortlist?

Date: .... Today: ....

....

....

Mindlessly fill this page
with perfect circles.

(Take inspiration from under your eyes.)

Date: _____   Today: _____

_____

_____

Use this space to make a print of your
baby's foot using nappy cream.

Date: .... Today: ....

....

....

Design a 'welcome to parenting' card.

Date: .... Today: ....

Before your baby wakes up from a nap, list the nine things you would like to do if you had a child-free day.

(Repetition of 'sleep' is restricted to three times.)

1. ....
2. ....
3. ....
4. ....
5. ....
6. ....
7. ....
8. ....
9. ....

Date: .... Today: ....

....

....

What's the one piece of advice you would give your child today, to be read when they turn twenty-one?

'Everybody knows how to raise children, except the people who have them.'

– P. J. O'Rourke

Date: .... Today: ....

....

....

The worst TV you've watched this month was:

1 ....
2 ....
3 ....
4 ....

The series you mainlined was:

Date: .... Today: ....

....

....

the perfect parent cake recipe

1. GO TO A BAKERY
2. BUY A CAKE
3. EAT THE CAKE

List five skills you don't have that
you would love your child to learn.

1. ....

2. ....

3. ....

4. ....

5. ....

'Your child will
follow your example,
not your advice.'

Date: ....   Today: ....
....
....

Ask a grandparent for their best piece of parenting advice and note it here.*

*Warning: make no promises
that you will follow this advice.

Date: _____ Today: _____

_____

_____

HERE ARE SOME DESIGNS THAT HAVE BEEN SHOWN TO STIMULATE EYESIGHT IN BOTH PARENTS AND VERY SMALL BABIES.

At what age did you become a parent?
What were the pros and cons?

Date: _____ Today: _____

_____

_____

Draw an outline of your hand here
and your child's in the middle.

The two of us, aged .... and ....

Date: .... Today: ....

What is the one parenting item
that you can't live without?

Did anything promise so much and deliver so little?

'A house with children runs on Love, Laughter and caffeine.'

Date: .... Today: ....

....

....

Which people around you do you admire as parents and why?

Date: _____ Today: _____

TAPE A LOCK OF YOUR CHILD'S HAIR HERE.

Date: _____ Today: _____

_____

_____

Do you have any traditions in your family that you would like to pass on?

Date: _____   Today: _____

_____

_____

Describe your ultimate date night.

(One day this may actually happen.)

Date: .... Today: ....

....

....

Smudge here the first solid food your baby ate.

What is it?

Date: .... Today: ....

....

....

Your child's favourite toy is:

Where or who is it from?

The date you lost it and all hell broke loose was:

Date: .... Today: ....
....
....

PARENTING REWARD CHART

	Had a shower	Washed your hair	Used both hands to eat
Monday			
Tuesday			
Wednesday			
Thursday			
Friday			
Saturday			
Sunday			

Avoided children's TV	Read a book	Woke up independently	Ate slowly

Date: .... Today: ....

....

....

DAILY ASSESSMENT

#parentingfails   #parentingwins

1 ....   1 ....

2 ....   2 ....

3 ....   3 ....

'The quickest way for a parent to get a child's attention is to sit down and look comfortable.'

– Lane Olinghouse

Date: ....   Today: ....

....

....

Create your ideal
playlist for parents.

Date: .... Today: ....

....

....

Your most magical parenting moment so far is:

Date: .... Today: ....

....

....

Your child's favourite foods (today) are:

1. ....
2. ....
3. ....
4. ....

Things they refuse to eat.

(Exclude obvious foodstuffs like lovingly home-made food.)

1. ....
2. ....
3. ....
4. ....

Date: ....   Today: ....

....

....

Draw your family members here.

'Be nice to your children for they will choose your rest home.'

– Phyllis Diller

Date: .... Today: ....

....

....

Use this page for your child's fingerprints.
Use whatever works or is already on
their hands. Options include yoghurt,
paint, snot or expensive make-up.

Date: .... Today: ....

....

....

Unscramble these words as you reminisce about the nicest meal you've ever eaten.

SEPA

btekrbicas
- -

tkractrocssi

AABNAN
- -

Umusmh

mruueccb
- -

benasedkba

nhifiresfgs
- -

OSATT

gyoturh
- -

Date: .... Today: ....

....

....

Place a hot drink that you intend to consume here.

When it goes cold, pour it away.
Repeat.

Date: ....   Today: ....

....

What are the things you love about looking after your child versus paid employment?

What are the things you love about paid employment versus childcare?

Date: .... Today: ....

....

....

PARENTING BINGO

CROSS OFF THESE THINGS IF YOU'VE
EXPERIENCED THEM THIS WEEK.
IF YOU COMPLETE YOUR BINGO
CARD, DRINK BEER OR WINE.

BINGO

Poonami	Nappy-changing wee	Vomiting	Baby food accident
Cluster feeding	Meltdown	All-night baby party	Teething

Describe the most ridiculous thing you've done to get your child to sleep.

Date: ....   Today: ....

....

....

Great Grandparents

Grandparents

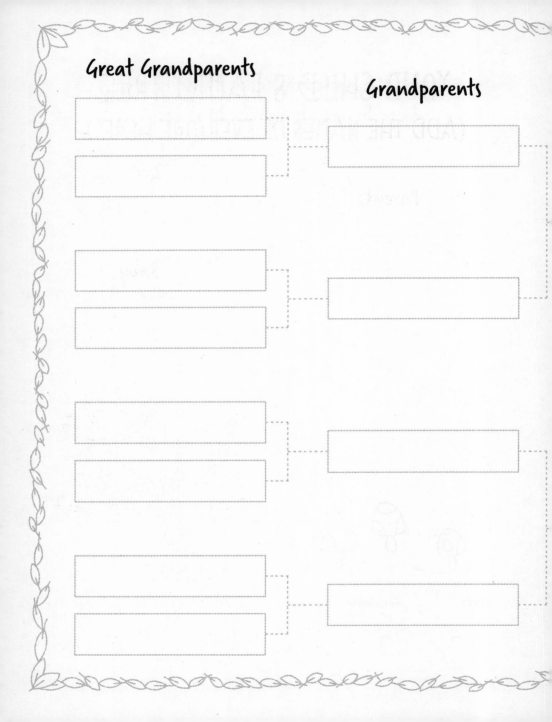

YOUR CHILD'S FAMILY TREE
(ADD THE NAMES OF EVERYONE HERE.)

Parents

Baby

Date: .... Today: ....

....

....

What songs do you sing to your child?

1 ....

2 ....

3 ....

4 ....

'Being a parent is the realization that you only know the first line to any nursery rhyme.'

Date: ....   Today: ....

....

The first holiday you took with your child was to:

It was:

☐ Successful

☐ Disastrous

☐ Redefined the word 'holiday'

Date: .... Today: ....

....

....

After your first month as a parent, what did you learn about yourself and your child?

Date: .... Today: ....

What song is number one this week?

Reward yourself with chocolate if you have any idea who the artist is.

Date: .... Today: ....

....

....

DRESS-UP DOLLY PARENT

DRAW CLOTHES ON THIS PARENT TO MAKE THEM EASILY IDENTIFIABLE.

Date: ....

Today: ....

Write an ode to beer or wine.

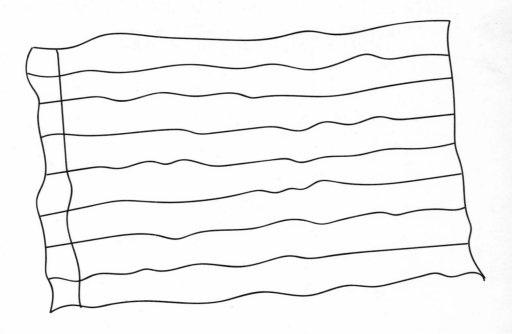

 'Warning: drinking alcoholic beverages before pregnancy can cause pregnancy.'

Date: .... Today: ....

....

....

Learn to sign your child's name.

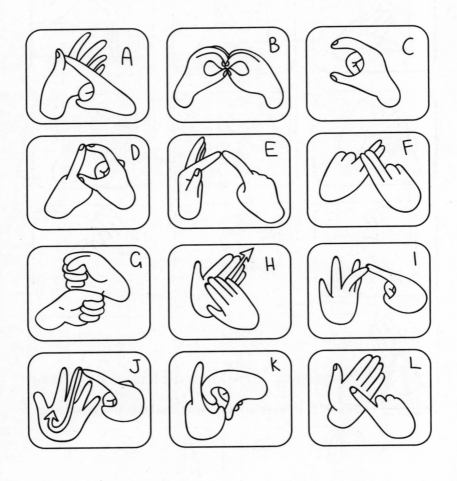

Date: _____   Today: _____

_____

_____

Someone who made my day easier was:

....

because:

....

....

....

....

....

'People who say they sleep like babies usually don't have one.'

– Leo J. Burke

Date: .... Today: ....

....

....

SLEEP SNAPSHOT

Slept from .... to ....

Woke up .... times.

I feel ....

Surely this ....

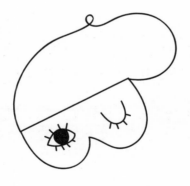

Date: ....   Today: ....

Draw your fantasy baby buggy here.

Date: .... Today: ....

....

....

Fill this page with mindless doodles because it's That Kind of Day/Night.

Date: _____   Today: _____

_____

_____

Record your child's most
momentous poonami episode
here for posterity.

RANKING:

1 2 3 4 5 6 7 8 9 10

1 = Minimal leakage.
10 = I threw away the entire
outfit, including my own.

Date: _____   Today: _____

_____

_____

Stick a receipt here that best sums up how you now spend your money. Try not to weep.

‘A parent is someone who has photos in their wallet where money used to be.’

Date: .... Today: ....

Write about the first night out you had
with friends since becoming a parent.

The hangover was:

Date: .... Today: ....

....

....

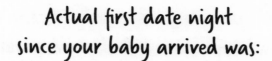

Actual first date night
since your baby arrived was:

'If your child goes to bed
two hours late they will
reward you by sleeping in for
approximately three minutes.'

Date: _____   Today: _____

_____

_____

Choose a happy day. List six reassuring things here for when the going gets tough:*

1.

2.

3.

4.

5.

6.

*Fold over the corner on this page.

Date: Today:

HAND-LUGGAGE CHECKLIST:

- ☐ Passport
- ☐ Tickets
- ☐ Nappies
- ☐ Nappy bags
- ☐ Baby wipes
- ☐ Changing mat
- ☐ Milk/snacks
- ☐ Bottles
- ☐ Dummy
- ☐ Comfort blanket
- ☐ Muslin cloths

- ☐ Spare outfit(s)
- ☐ Phone
- ☐ Charger
- ☐ Travel adapter
- ☐ Toys
- ☐ Books
- ☐ Printed travel details/phone numbers
- ☐ Medicine
- ☐ The patience of a saint

Date: .... Today: ....

....

....

Draw your house.

Who are your neighbours?

Date: .... Today: ....

Write a haiku about caffeine or cake
(line one: five syllables; line two: seven
syllables; line three: five syllables).

Date: .... Today: ....

....

....

SPOT THE DIFFERENCE

Write a postcard to your future self.

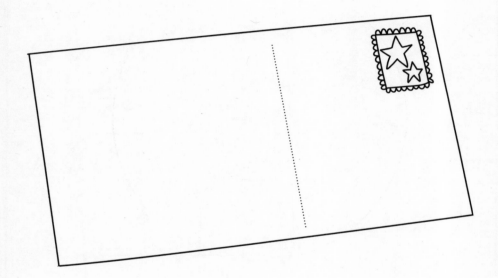

Date: .... Today: ....

....

....

Create a 'parent' emoji.

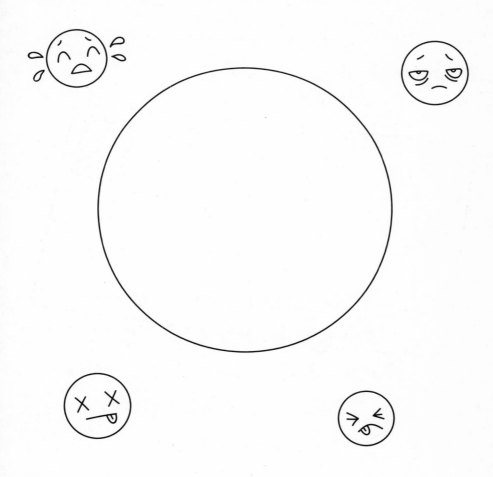

Date: _____ Today: _____

_____

_____

Complete this in your own words.

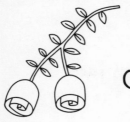

Roses are red,

Parenting is .... ,

....

....

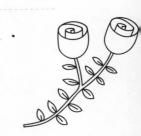

'You can learn many
things from children.
How much patience you
have, for example.'

– Franklin P. Adams

Date: .... Today: ....

....

....

Add common 'parenting' features to this face.

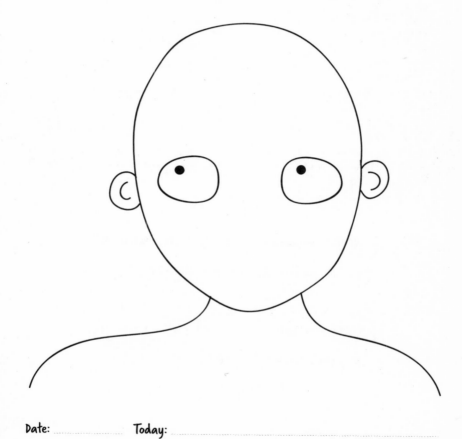

Date: .... Today: ....

....

....

ARE YOU MORE LIKELY TO:

A. SLEEP   B. SEX
A. GIN   B. JUICE
A. BOX SET   B. BOX FIT
A. TAKEAWAY   B. TABLE FOR TWO
A. BATHTIME   B. BAR TIME
A. TRACKSUIT BOTTOMS B. TAILORED TROUSERS
A. BEDTIME STORY   B. LATEST BESTSELLER

If you answered mostly As, you are
a fully qualified parent.

If you answered mostly Bs, you are
a parenting work-in-progress.

Date: ....   Today: ....

....

Design a tattoo to reflect your parenting experience.

'Having a child is liking getting
a tattoo . . . on your face.
You better be committed.'
– *Eat Pray Love* (screenplay)

Date: .... Today: ....

....

....

Make a list of things you can talk to your friends
about that aren't related to your child.

Date: _____ Today: _____

_____

_____

Name the places that mean something to you where you would like to take your child.

In their neighbourhood:

In their home town:

In the world:

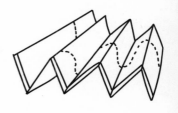

Date: .... Today: ....

....

....

In the small window between your child and you going to bed,* what do you do?

*For your own sanity, never compare how long this time is with other parents.

Date: _____ Today: _____

_____

Tick off these modes of transport as you master travelling with a small person:

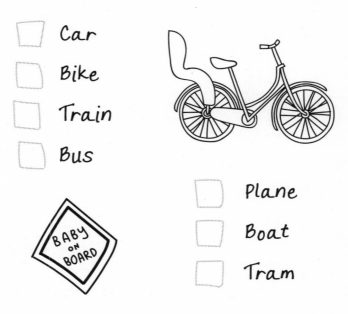

☐ Car
☐ Bike
☐ Train
☐ Bus

☐ Plane
☐ Boat
☐ Tram

'If you want to know what a child has eaten for the past year, remove their car seat.'

What were your five favourite books as a child that you look forward to sharing?

1. ....

2. ....

3. ....

4. ....

5. ....

Date: .... Today: ....

....

Draw a picture here using red wine and a cork like a stamp.

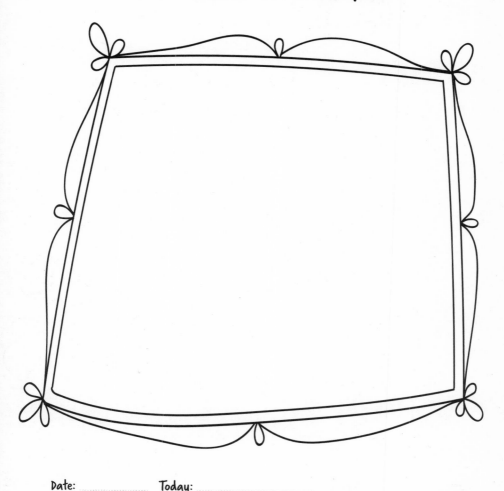

Date: .... Today: ....

....

....

The best meals to eat with one hand (probably your unnatural one) are:

Decorate this mug with an encouraging quote for parents.

Date: _____ Today: _____

_____

COMPLETE THIS WORD SEARCH.

alarm clock

cinema

disposable income

gin

golf

impromptu

lie in

pelvic floor

pub

quickie

rested

shower

spa day

spontaneous

sunday

vodka

'Children make it difficult to be the parent you always imagined you would be.'

Date: _____ Today: _____

a	x	d	a	l	a	r	m	c	l	o	c	k	d	s	e	y	o	e	t
e	d	u	e	i	a	r	t	p	o	t	u	o	p	t	o	w	h	o	e	e
a	t	i	i	t	y	n	o	r	p	a	o	o	k	i	n	i	b	e	i
d	i	s	p	o	s	a	b	l	e	i	n	c	o	m	e	u	e	g	t
v	n	t	a	g	o	e	i	l	e	t	m	l	g	e	p	r	o	d	n
o	e	o	o	g	y	s	r	u	a	p	i	p	h	m	r	r	h	h	a
e	i	e	t	e	m	c	h	n	p	e	c	b	r	h	a	w	c	r	t
p	p	h	a	t	d	o	e	o	i	h	t	o	s	o	h	t	e	e	a
t	e	h	r	o	f	o	k	n	w	d	o	t	y	t	m	t	d	b	t
e	s	l	e	e	u	a	h	b	e	e	o	a	e	a	a	p	d	r	r
s	t	r	v	s	s	e	d	t	i	s	r	t	a	l	d	a	t	h	f
e	u	c	y	i	h	r	a	t	t	t	d	f	f	t	i	n	s	u	h
u	n	e	i	k	c	i	u	q	e	s	c	e	l	a	o	w	u	e	o
r	n	h	s	o	t	f	e	s	n	o	h	r	o	s	k	s	a	s	b
l	c	g	d	c	e	o	l	a	p	h	t	a	g	w	t	n	r	f	w
a	e	w	r	w	a	s	n	o	a	a	l	r	p	s	o	t	i	t	b
e	k	o	r	a	t	g	t	g	o	e	d	e	f	s	i	s	a	s	h
i	a	d	n	i	g	b	n	t	h	r	t	a	f	d	r	a	i	a	o
w	s	p	o	v	e	m	a	i	o	d	e	p	y	c	i	n	e	m	a
i	f	w	d	v	g	c	h	o	s	r	o	a	n	a	n	a	n	o	s

What are the things that strangers say to you most often when you are with your child?

Date: .... Today: ....

Write a funny story about being a parent using these words: happy, question, wine, walk, chocolate, bottle, dream, imagine.

Date: .... Today: ....

Stick a leaf from each season here to reassure yourself at 3 a.m. that time is actually passing.

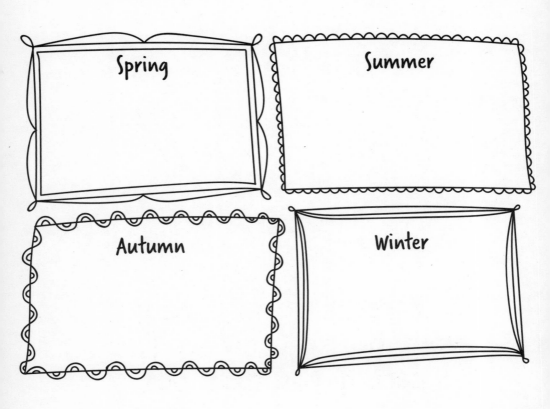

Spring

Summer

Autumn

Winter

Date: _____   Today: _____

_____

Design a label for
Parent Gin here.

'Parents don't care if
your house is clean. They
care if you have gin.'

Date: _____ Today: _____

List major world events that happen this year.

Date: _____ Today: _____

Create your own date
night at home.*

☐ Cinema - buy some popcorn
boxes and make popcorn. Pretend your
TV is 100 times bigger than it is.

☐ Make cocktails and mocktails
and drink them by candlelight.

☐ Play cards. Instead of money,
play for back massages.

☐ Set up a romantic dining table and
order a takeaway to dine in.

☐ Put on your finest gear
and take selfies.

☐ ....

....

* Do not talk about parenting for
the duration of these evenings.

ASK YOUR PARTNER OR
FRIEND TO WRITE SOMETHING
ABOUT YOU AS A PARENT ON
THE NEXT PAGE. FOLD THIS
PAGE CLOSED VERTICALLY
AND LEAVE UNTIL YOU
REALLY NEED TO READ IT.

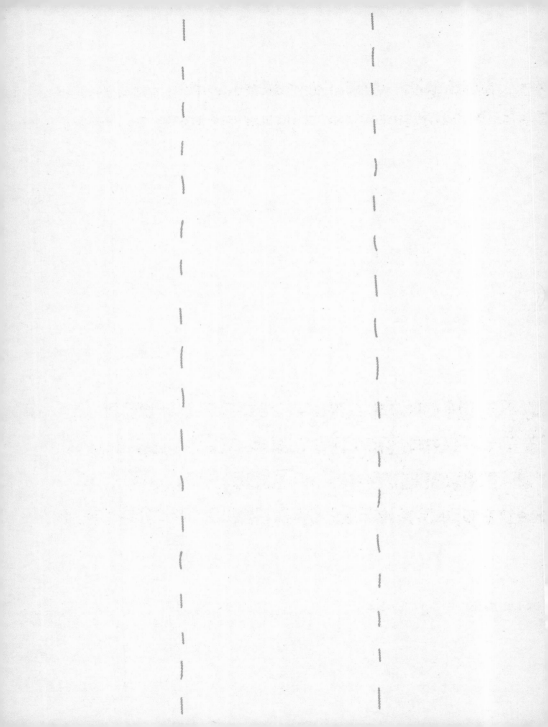

List five reasons why you are a great parent.

1. ....

2. ....

3. ....

4. ....

5. ....

'Being a parent is the only time you can experience heaven and hell at the same time.'

Date: ....   Today: ....

....

....

COCKTAIL CROSSWORD

ACROSS

3. Orange peel perfection

4. Frisky holiday time pre-children

5. Hangover cure of champions

6. Salty or sweet . . .

7. New York, New York

8. With a twist

DOWN

1. For when you're a peach

2. Worldly wise

6. If you're minted . . .

Date: _____   Today: _____

_____

_____

Design a T-shirt for parents.

Date: .... Today: ....

....

....

THE MOST CHALLENGING
TIME OF DAY IS:

HOW TO TELL THE TIME

A.M.

P.M.

Date: .... Today: ....

CREATE YOUR OWN SNAKES AND LADDERS GAME.

32	33 Buggy breakdown	34	35
31	30	29	28
16	17	18	19
15	14 No one cries for 2 hours	13	12
START	1	2	3

5

37
Poonami
episode!

38

FINISH

z z z

26

25

24

22

23

21

10
Gin

9 . . . .

8

5

6

7

WINE-TASTING NOTES

WINE:	DATE:	NOTES:
Sauvignon Blanc		Bloody delicious
Valpolicella		Bloody delicious
Chardonnay		Bloody delicious
Pinot Gris		Bloody delicious
Soave		Bloody delicious
Rioja		Bloody delicious
Pinot Noir		Bloody delicious

'The most expensive part of parenting is all the wine you have to drink.'

Date: .... Today: ....

Describe the perfect play date for parents.

Date: _____ Today: _____

Draw your child's first tooth that came through here.

'Teething babies are so much fun. Said no parent ever.'

Date: .... Today: ....

....

....

List everything you now use baby wipes for as you ponder how you ever existed without them.

'ALL of us have moments in our lives that test our courage. Taking children into a house with a white carpet is one of them.'

– Erma Bombeck

Date: .... Today: ....

....

....

What are your top tips for staying awake?

Fail-proof way to cure insomnia.
1. Have children.

Date: _____   Today: _____
_____
_____

In the middle of the night, your favourite apps or websites are:

1. ....
2. ....
3. ....
4. ....
5. ....
6. ....
7. ....
8. ....
9. ....

Date: ....   Today: ....

....

Invent a parent superhero.

Date: _____   Today: _____

_____

_____

Which of these parenting superpowers have you acquired?

☐ Eating with your opposite hand

☐ Picking up things with your toes

☐ Getting ready for bed in the dark

☐ Having a shower in less than three minutes

Add your own:

Date: _____ Today: _____

_____

_____

PARENT MAZE

Start →

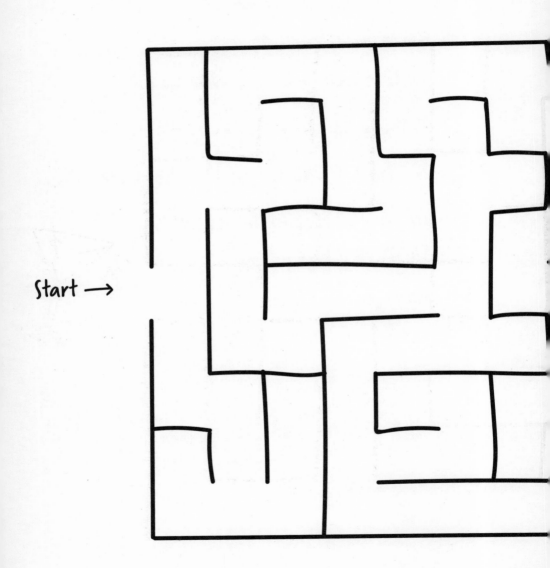

Redesign the cover of this journal here.

Date: .... Today: ....

....

....

What was the name of your favourite toy as a child?

Do you still have it to pass on to your child?

Date: .... Today: ....

....

....

The things you shouldn't have wasted
time doing before you had children:

1 ....
2 ....
3 ....
4 ....

'A parent is someone who
trades in functioning
brain cells for children.'

Date: ....   Today: ....
....
....

Colour in this bouquet of flowers for yourself.

Date: .... Today: ....

....

Engrave this trophy to yourself.

Date: .... Today: ....

Illustrate your baby's current hairstyle here.

Date: .... Today: ....

....

....

DOT-TO-DOT

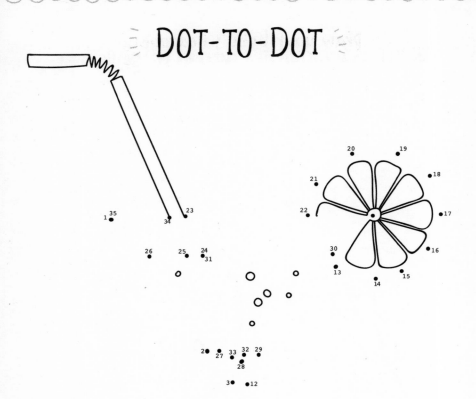

Draw your baby's bedroom.

Date: .... Today: ....

....

....

If parenting were a sport it would be:

....

because:

Date: ....   Today: ....
....
....

Design a remote control for your child.

Date: _____ Today: _____

_____

After your first three months as a parent, what did you learn about yourself and your child?

Date: .... Today: ....

Open a book at random and write the
first sentence you see here. This is your
parenting motto for today.*

*or not.

Date: .... Today: ....

....

....

Create a design of anything you like here.

'Parenting is about sacrificing everything. Other than wine, chocolate and caffeine.'

Date: _____ Today: _____
_____

If you could have a magical wish granted it would be:

Date: _____ Today: _____

_____

_____

Things you took for granted before becoming a parent were:

1. ....
2. ....
3. ....
4. ....
5. ....
6. ....
7. ....
8. ....

Date: .... Today: ....

....

....

Decorate this box of chocolates for yourself.

Date: _____ Today: _____

_____

_____

What regular events do you take your baby to each week?

....

....

PARENT RHYME TIME

If you're happy and you know it, drink some gin,
If you're happy and you know it, drink some gin,
If you're happy and you know it, and
you really want to show it,
If you're happy and you know it, drink some gin!

Date: .... Today: ....

....

....

HOW MUCH HAS CHANGED?

How much does your baby weigh today?

Age:

Your baby's eye colour is:

Your baby's hair colour is:

Date: Today:

Draw stars all over this page.

Date: .... Today: ....

....

....

Invent a parent-inspired cocktail menu.

Date: ....   Today: ....

....

....

Plan a child-free day out.

_____

_____

_____

_____

_____

_____

'We may not be able to
prepare the future for our
children, but we can prepare
our children for the future.'

– Franklin D. Roosevelt

Date: _____ Today: _____

Write your to-do list.

Date: ....   Today: ....

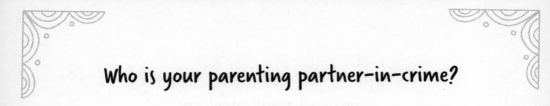

Who is your parenting partner-in-crime?

Write a letter to them here.

How, if at all, has being a parent changed your view on:

World peace:

Instant coffee:

Ready meals:

Recycling:

Box sets:

Leggings:

Children's TV:

Date: .... Today: ....

....

Draw something you can see right now.

Date: _____ Today: _____

_____

_____

Doodle your favourite things on this page.

Date: .... Today: ....

....

....

BABY MAZE

Start →

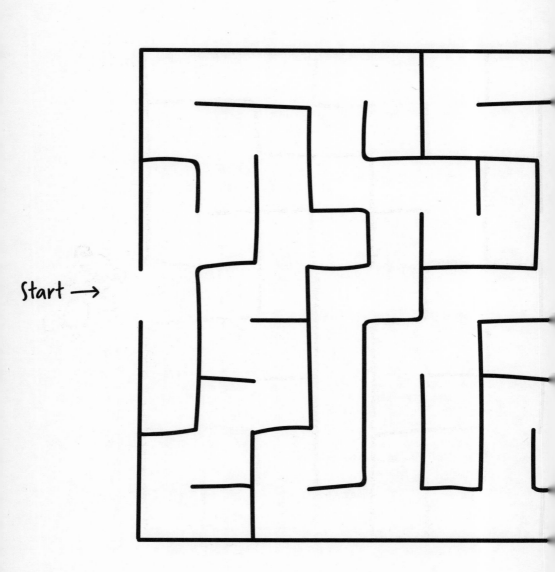

BEST baby food recipe

....

....

....

....

....

....

....

....

....

....

....

....

....

Date: .... Today: ....

....

....

What things would you recommend to give to a new parent?

1. Gin
2.
3.
4.
5.
6.
7.
8.
9.

Date: .... Today: ....

....

....

My biggest fear is . . .

Date: .... Today: ....

....

....

MORNING TIREDNESS TEST
FORGOT TO:

- [ ] Brush teeth
- [ ] Eat breakfast
- [ ] Brush hair
- [ ] Take keys
- [ ] Drink tea/coffee*
- [ ] Take purse/wallet

* trick question

Date: _____   Today: _____

_____

_____

List five things your child does that you would like to do if it were socially acceptable.

1. ....
2. ....
3. ....
4. ....
5. ....

....

Date: .... Today: ....

....

....

Find someone to play noughts and crosses with.

Date: ....   Today: ....

....

....

Plan a world trip for you and your child.
Why would you take them to these places?

Date: .... Today: ....

....

....

What makes your baby smile or giggle?

What makes them cry?

'Children are like wet cement:
whatever falls on them
makes an impression.'
– Haim Ginott

Date: .... Today: ....

....

....

List seven things that have changed about parenting since you were a child.

1. ....

2. ....

3. ....

4. ....

5. ....

6. ....

7. ....

....

....

Date: ....   Today: ....

....

....

Draw the chocolate cake of your sleep-deprived dreams.

Date: .... Today: ....

....

....

Write a rhyming poem using these words:
nappy, vodka, toes, child, play, sleep.

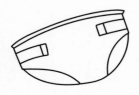

Date: .... Today: ....

....

....

If your child were to be raised by five famous people from all of history, who would they be and why?

1. ....
2. ....
3. ....
4. ....
5. ....

Date: .... Today: ....

....

....

Put your crawling child on a playmat and track their movements in the next ten minutes.

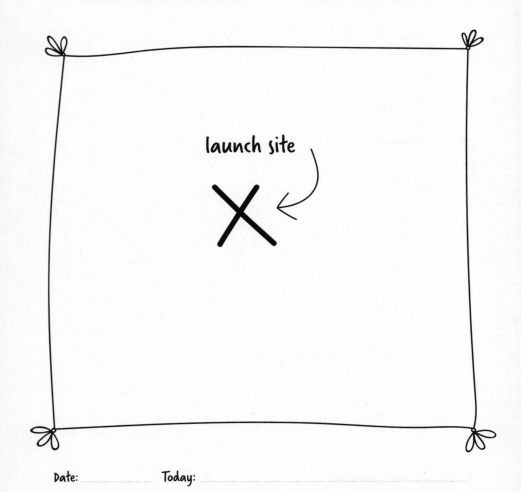

launch site

X

Date: _____   Today: _____

_____

_____

Illustrate a designer-edition nappy.

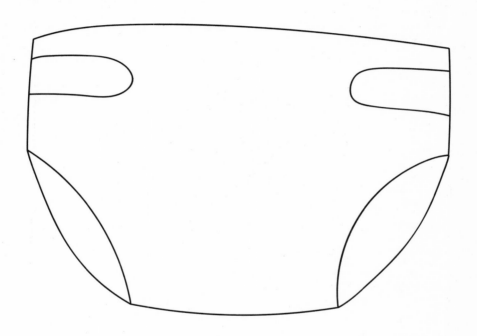

Date: .... Today: ....

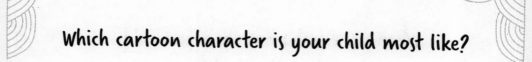

Which cartoon character is your child most like?

When your baby has their first cold,
draw how YOU feel here.

'To be a parent you need
three bones: a wishbone, a
backbone and a funny bone.'

Date: .... Today: ....

....

....

Draw the route you take with the buggy to get your baby to sleep.

This is your house

Date: ....   Today: ....

....

....

Based on their personality now, what job do you think your child might have when they grow up?

Date: .... Today: ....

....

....

Annotate this parent with all your aches and pains.

Date: ....   Today: ....

....

....

Draw your favourite outfit
your child has here.

And the most impractical.

'The only thing kids
wear out faster than
shoes is their parents.'

– John J. Plomp

Date: .... Today: ....
....
....

Draw and label ten items that you
would put in a Parent Time Capsule,
to be opened in the year 3000.

Date: .... Today: ....

What do you do on a rainy day?*

*other than weep and drink wine.

Date: _____ Today: _____

_____

_____

Design the ideal parent mobile
to hang above your bed.

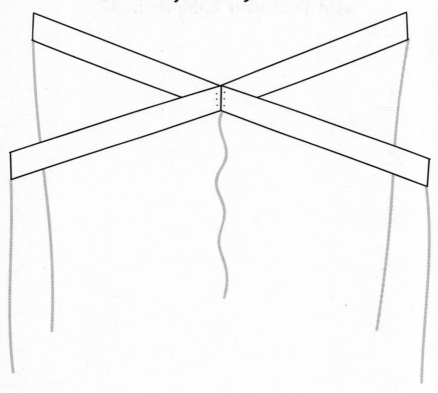

Date: .... Today: ....

....

....

What have you not purchased or used since your baby arrived?

1. ....

2. ....

3. ....

4. ....

5. ....

6. ....

Date: .... Today: ....

....

....

Draw an aerial map of a fantasy parent soft play.

Date: .... Today: ....

....

....

List the six things you repeatedly
talk to other parents about.

1. ....
2. ....
3. ....
4. ....
5. ....
6. ....

'Children are happy because
they don't have a file in their
mind called "ALL the Things
That Could Go Wrong".'

– Marianne Williamson

Date: .... Today: ....

....

....

Use these clock faces to predict the times your baby will wake up tonight. Update in a different colour with the actual times. If you get any correct, drink wine as a reward.

Date: .... Today: ....

Design the ultimate high chair for your child.*

*Self-cleaning, obviously.

Date: _____ Today: _____

_____

_____

If your child has a period
of sleep regression, scribble
your frustration here. *

*You may need all the coffee.

Date: _____ Today: _____

_____

_____

Divide this circle into a pie chart
of what you did today.

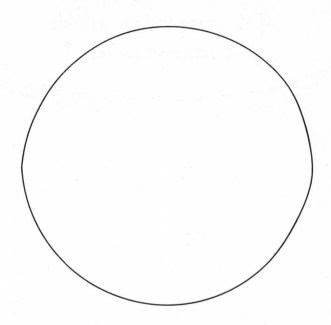

'Great parenting lies
somewhere between "don't
do that" and "ah, whatever".'

Date: .... Today: ....

....

....

What life-changing gadgets would you invent to make life easier?

Date: _____ Today: _____

....

....

Write a letter to yourself about what lack of sleep really feels like.

Date: _____ Today: _____

_____

_____

I am always amazed that . . .

Date: .... Today: ....

....

....

After your first six months as a parent, what have you learned about yourself and your child?

Date: _____ Today: _____

_____

_____

Where do you like to go for walks while your child sleeps in their buggy?

1. ....

2. ....

3. ....

4. ....

5. ....

Date: ....   Today: ....

....

....

Draw a cartoon strip of today.

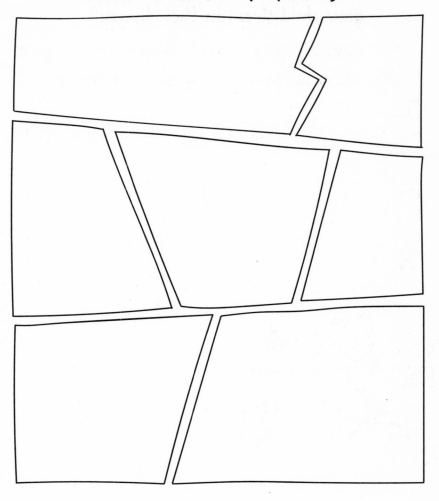

Date: .... Today: ....

....

....

THE SLEEPSUIT CHALLENGE

Time yourself once a week as you wrestle your baby into a sleepsuit. See if you get faster . . .

Week 1: ....

Week 2: ....

Week 3: ....

Week 4: ....

Date: .... Today: ....

The new friends you made
because of your child are:

'A friend of wine is a
friend of mine.'

Date: .... Today: ....

....

....

How did you wean your child on to solid food?

It was _____ % less 'fun' than I thought it would be.

When it's over I never want to see a _____

_____ again.

The ready-made food I rely on like the air I

breathe is _____ .

Date: _____   Today: _____

'Isn't it funny how day by day nothing changes, but when you look back everything is different.'

– C. S. Lewis

How much does your baby weigh today?

....

Age: ....

Your baby's eye colour is: ....

Your baby's hair colour is: ....

Date: .... Today: ....

....

....

Write a song about your child to the tune
of 'Twinkle, Twinkle, Little Star'.

'Music to a parent's
ears is a baby snoring.'

Date: _____ Today: _____

_____

_____

If your baby had a warning label what would it say?

⚠️ WARNING

DESCRIBE HOW YOUR CHILD . . .

Moves about:

Sleeps:

Date: .... Today: ....

....

....

Laughs:

DESCRIBE HOW YOUR CHILD

Plays:

Eats:

WORD ASSOCIATION

baby

nappy

cry

feed

bottle

wine

Date: .... Today: ....

....

....

Things they don't tell you about being a parent:

....

....

....

....

....

....

'90% of parenting is asking: "Why is this wet?".'

Date: ....   Today: ....

....

COLOUR BY NUMBERS

1 – Red
2 – Light Blue
3 – Green
4 – Yellow
5 – Dark Red
6 – Purple
7 – Pink
8 – Dark Blue
9 – Grey
10– Orange

RESOLUTIONS FOR THIS WEEK

'In parenting the days are long but the years are short . . .'

Date: ....   Today: ....

....

....

INTERESTING CONVERSATIONS YOU'VE OVERHEARD

Date: ....   Today: ....

....

....

Spray some perfume here for when the nappy smells get too bad.

Date: .... Today: ....

....

....

Last night I dreamt that . . .

Was I actually asleep?

Date: _____   Today: _____

_____

_____

PEOPLE WATCHING
TICK THE BOX WHEN YOU SEE:

- ☐ Baby asleep (preferably yours)
- ☐ Child with a dummy
- ☐ Another adult
- ☐ A parent with an unruly kid (preferably NOT yours)
- ☐ A postman
- ☐ Someone with more baggage than you
- ☐ A barman

Date: .... Today: ....

....

....

After your first nine months as a parent, what did you learn about yourself and your child?

Date: .... Today: ....

....

Write down what's on your mind.

Date: .... Today: ....

....

....

Make a picture from this.

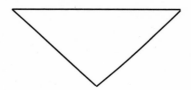

Date: .... Today: ....

Draw these shapes without taking your pen off the page.

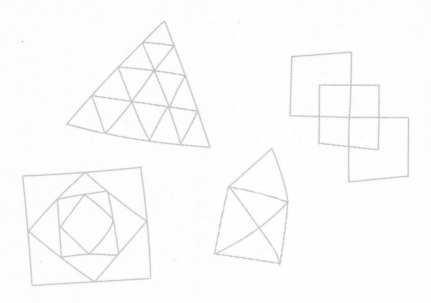

'Becoming a parent makes you realize you can do almost anything one-handed.'

Date: .... Today: ....

What did you do for your child's first birthday celebration? Who came?

Tick this box if you remembered to celebrate your own birthday this year.

Date: .... Today: ....

....

....

Write a message for help here using Morse code.

A ●▬   F ●●▬●

B ▬●●●   G ▬▬●

C ▬●▬●   H ●●●●

D ▬●●   I ●●

E ●   J ●▬▬▬

Date: ....   Today: ....

K	— • —	S	• • •
L	• — • •	T	—
M	— —	U	• • —
N	— •	V	• • • —
O	— — —	W	• — —
P	• — — •	X	— • • —
Q	— — • —	Y	— • — —
R	• — •	Z	— — • •

What was the best experience you had
dining out with your child?

What one thing could all restaurants/
cafes do to make parents' lives easier?

Date: .... Today: ....

....

....

If you could live anywhere else in the world with your child, where would it be and why?

Date: ....   Today: ....

....

....

Get your child to make some artwork here.

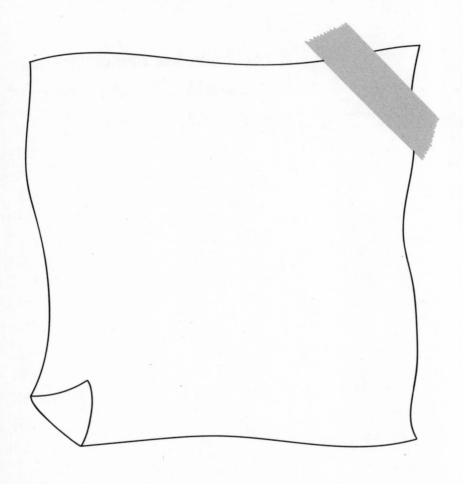

Date: ....   Today: ....

Write your parenting bucket list here.

Date: .... Today: ....

....

....

Use the letters in your baby's name
for words that describe your day.

'The sole purpose of a
child's middle name is
so they can tell when
they're truly in trouble.'

Date: _____ Today: _____

Paint or decorate the nails on this hand.

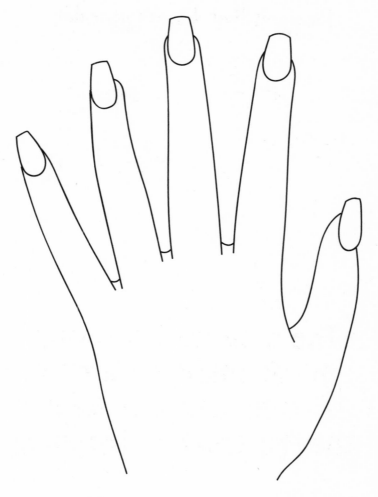

Date: .... Today: ....

....

....

Write a headline and short news article about your child's latest achievement.

Date: _____ Today: _____

_____

_____

PARENTING DICTIONARY
MAKE UP YOUR OWN WORDS TO DESCRIBE THESE THINGS.

- The dilemma when you're holding a sleeping baby and the doorbell rings:

- The poo that escapes from a nappy:

- When you have to keep pushing your buggy so your baby doesn't wake up:

- The white stains on your shoulder from dribble/vomit:

- That moment right before your child starts crying:

- The panic when you misplace your child's favourite toy:

- The shower you have when you're on borrowed baby time:

After your first year as a parent, what have you learned about yourself and your child?

Date: _____ Today: _____

_____

_____

USE THE FOLLOWING PARENTING MILESTONE PAGES FOR SELFIES THAT BEST CAPTURE THE MOMENT. SHARE THEM WITH #IMWRECKEDJOURNAL

THIS IS WHAT PARENTING LOOKS LIKE

#nofilter
#imwreckedjournal

PROUD PARENTING MOMENT

#lovemychild
#imwreckedjournal

SOS. BRING WINE!

#longestdayknown
tomankind
#imwreckedjournal

THIS IS THE FACE OF SLEEP DEPRIVATION

#sosososotired
#imwreckedjournal

MAKING PARENTING LOOK EASY

#forthissecondonly
#imwreckedjournal